Butterflies
of Jamaica

Butterflies
of Jamaica

Eric Garraway and Audette J. A. Bailey

MACMILLAN
CARIBBEAN

Macmillan Education
Between Towns Road, Oxford OX4 3PP
A division of Macmillan Publishers Limited
Companies and representatives throughout the world

www.macmillan-caribbean.com

ISBN 0-333-99255-5

First published 2005

Designed by Amanda Easter Design Limited
Illustrated by Tek Art
All photographs by Eric Garraway except
p.17 (*Danaus eresimus eresimus*), p.26 (*Adelpha abyla*), p.91 (*Chioides catillus
churchi*) by Dr J Woodley.
Cover design by Gary Fielder at AC Design
Cover photographs by Eric Garraway

Printed and bound in Thailand

2009 2008 2007 2006 2005
10 9 8 7 6 5 4 3 2 1

Contents

Dedication

Special thanks to my wife Seneca, who tolerated my absence on my long excursion to the field.

Acknowledgements

This work started when Dr John P Parnell, then of the University of the West Indies (UWI), invited me to join him on one of his expeditions to study the endangered Jamaica Giant Swallowtail. John has remained a source of inspiration and a friend.

The Department of Life Sciences, UWI, has been very supportive and the people of the towns of Millbank and Comfort Castle, Portland, embraced us as their own – a special thanks to Errol Francis who was our field assistant. Members of the Natural History Society of Jamaica (NHSJ), being aware of the need for field guides, offered encouragement and many of the photographs were taken on field trips of the NHSJ's Butterfly Group.

Eric Garraway

Abbreviations and Definitions

CITES   Convention for International Trade on Endangered
            Species of Wild Fauna and Flora
End   Endemic
End/Sub   Endemic subspecies
Endangered (as defined by the IUCN) A taxa in danger of extinction and
            whose survival is unlikely if the causal factors continue
            operating. Included are taxa whose numbers have been
            reduced to a critical level or whose habitats have been so
            drastically reduced that they are deemed to be in immediate
            danger of extinction. Included here are taxa that are possibly
            already extinct but have definitely been seen in the wild in the
            past 50 years.
IUCN   International Union for the Conservation of Nature and
            Natural resources
NEPA   Natural Environment Planning Agency
Vulnerable (as defined by the IUCN) A taxa believed likely to move into
            the endangered category in the near future if the causal factors
            continue operating.

Introduction

Butterflies have long been one of mankind's favourite insects. They have earned a special place because of their rich blend of nature's colours, their graceful flight and their association with gardens. Today, they are being used as an environmental indicator species. They are also becoming more important as a 'flagship species' in biodiversity and conservation programs and, as such, contribute extensively to the survival of 'obscure species'.

No other group of insects on Jamaica is as well documented as the butterflies. However, the available books on the subject do not answer many of the questions asked by the non-biologist and they are often not in a field guide format. The aim in producing this book is to provide a field guide that covers the more common species, as well as a few famous, but less common ones, while at the same time answering many of the questions the non-biologist asks. Because pinned specimens generally appear different from live insects, almost all photographs included in this book are of insects in the wild. This book does not provide taxonomic and systematic analyses; such information is available in more detailed books such as Riley (1975), Brown and Heineman (1972) and Smith *et al* (1994).

Biology and Ecology of Butterflies

Life history of butterflies

The life cycle of a butterfly has four main stages: egg, larva, pupa and adult. The appearance, shape and duration of each stage is characteristic of the given species. The adult is what is generally called the butterfly. Once it reaches this phase, there is no further increase in size. There is no such thing as a baby butterfly. The baby is, in fact, the larva, or caterpillar.

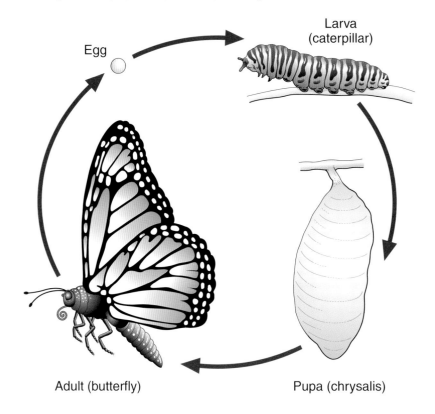

Egg

Larva (caterpillar)

Pupa (chrysalis)

Adult (butterfly)

Life cycle of a butterfly

Each butterfly selects a particular species or group of plants and a particular place on the plant to oviposit its eggs. Moreover, the eggs may be laid singly or in clusters, *e.g.* the Citrus Swallowtail lays its eggs singly on the young leaves and stems of citrus plants; the Giant Swallowtail on the upper surfaces of both young and old leaves of two species of *Hernandia*; the Monarch on the under surface of the leaves of milk weeds; the Lignum vitae butterfly in clusters on the upper surface of *Lignum vitae* leaves; while the Cloudless Sulphur lays its eggs in clusters on the flower buds and very young leaves of *Cassia* (*Senna*).

The egg hatches to a larva, or caterpillar. In many species, the larva's first meal is the remains of the egg, which is rich in nutrients. The larva goes through a series of stages (five to six in most cases) termed 'instars'. The shedding of the old larval skin, or cuticle, and its replacement with a new and bigger one marks the change from one instar to the next.

In some species, the appearance of the larva remains unchanged from instar to instar, but, in others, there might be dramatic changes. Most larvae feed at night. They remain motionless by day, relying upon their colouring and overall shapes for protection from would-be predators.

The pupa is a strange phase which does not feed and appears lifeless and inactive. In actual fact, on the inside, there is a great deal of activity, as larval tissues are being reorganised into adult tissues. The pupa generally has a hard outer covering which is important for its protection since it is unable to escape from predators. The shape and colour are generally characteristic of each species and often allow for blending into the habitat.

About one day before the pupa hatches, the adult butterfly may become visible through the pupal skin. Finally, the pupal skin splits open and the adult butterfly emerges. At this stage the wings are folded, much like a wet handkerchief. However, the pumping of blood through the veins soon expands them. The fully expanded wings dry slowly and the butterfly hangs almost motionless until they are fully dried. Once the wings are dry, the butterfly is ready for flight.

One of the main functions of the adult is to reproduce, a process that demands much energy from both sexes. Males may expend much energy in search of mates. In some groups they actively patrol areas (territories) in search of females. In other cases they perch where they are likely to encounter females and dart out to investigate potential mates – often any moving object of a suitable size – other butterfly species, birds, and even falling leaves!

Once contact is established with a female, she is courted. Courtship may involve visual stimuli (such as dance and display of colours), tactile stimuli (stroking with antennae and wings), and chemical stimuli (special 'perfumes' called pheromones). If he is accepted, copulation follows. Butterflies are often seen in mating pairs, the female, generally, being the active flyer, dragging the male along.

During copulation, the male not only passes sperm to the female but also a package full of nutrients which she will later use to help in the production of the eggs. This is unlike most other animals where the male's contribution to the production of the embryo is simply the sperm.

How long do butterflies live?

The duration of each stage of the life cycle varies from species to species. The length of time it takes for the egg to develop into an adult ranges from 17–18 days in species such as the Jamaican Mestra and the Cabbage Butterfly, to three months in species such as the Giant Swallowtail. The length of the adult life has not been accurately determined for many species. However, the estimates for tropical butterflies range from five days to seven months.

What do butterflies eat?

With a few exceptions, butterfly larvae are herbivorous. The food plant is generally specific – some larvae feeding on only one species of plant, others on plants belonging to the same family or, less commonly, on plants from related families. The larvae may also specialise on one particular part of the plant – that on which they feed, for example, old leaves, young leaves, young stems, buds, flowers, developing seeds or fruit. Butterfly larvae generally consume vast quantities of food. Any excess nutrients are stored in an organ called the 'fatbody' and it is this store of food that sustains the adult of those few species that do not feed as adults.

Adults generally feed on nectar from flowers and juices from fruit. Most feed on a wide variety of flowers or fruits, although they may show preferences. The fluid is collected through a long proboscis which, when not in use, is kept coiled under the head – the butterfly, in effect, carries its own drinking straw. The Heliconids are unique in that pollen is a very important part of their diet.

Both larvae and adults may drink water. The adults of some species congregate at puddles and drink, while larvae of species such as *Papilio homerus* drink raindrops from the surfaces of leaves.

Amongst those species whose larvae are not herbivorous is the Lycaenid family of butterflies. These produce caterpillars which secrete a sweet substance (honeydew) much relished by ants. The ants, in turn, protect the caterpillar from potential predators. However, some predatory Lycaenids exploit this relationship by inducing the ants to take them into their nests and then, rather than supplying honeydew, feed on the larvae of the ants.

Colours and vision

All stages of the life cycle are famous for their colours. These colours may be the results of pigmentation, and/or deposits of special waste products, or the refraction of light. Light passing through ribbed structures, or very thin, slightly separated layers, is refracted to give a variety of colours. Shades of blue, in particular, are produced in this way. In the adult butterfly, the colours are concentrated in tiny structures called scales. Scales appear as the coloured dust on your fingers after you have touched a butterfly's wings.

Butterflies have excellent vision. Their visual spectrum extends from the ultraviolet through red and so encompasses that of man and other insects. This is the broadest visible spectrum known in the animal kingdom. Ultraviolet vision is very important to butterflies – species that look very similar to us are remarkably different in UV light.

Not only do they have excellent colour discrimination across this wide spectrum, but they also have high sensitivity to movement and flickering. A butterfly's angle of vision is also very wide and so they are very difficult to approach from any direction. This, of course, is of little comfort to the collector, photographer or predator!

Butterflies' natural enemies

Butterflies' enemies include birds, lizards, predatory wasps, parasitic wasps and flies, spiders, beetles, mites, bacteria, viruses, nematodes and fungi, but they, in turn, have developed an array of protective mechanisms.

Birds feed on all stages of the life cycle. Flycatchers are likely to take adults while those species feeding on branches and leaves (*e.g.* some warblers) will collect eggs, larvae and pupae. Lizards have also been recorded taking butterflies, sometimes much larger than themselves. They take hold of the body, the wings are rubbed off on the vegetation and the body is eventually swallowed.

Mestra showing wings with a portion missing as the result of an attack by a bird or lizard.

Several species of wasps including the 'red wasps' (paper wasp, *Polistes*) the Euminid wasp *Pachodynerus nasidens* (which make nests in hollowed stems and keyholes etc. around the house) collect larvae. Beetles and spiders also take large quantities of small larvae, especially at night when most larvae are active.

Jamaican Satyra butterfly caught by a Crab Spider. Crab Spiders sit on flowers waiting for butterflies to come and feed. They often resemble parts of the flower.

There are several tiny wasps termed 'parasitoids' that attack butterflies. Some parasitoids attack the larvae, some the eggs, while others attack the pupae. Parasitoids generally have a long ovipositor, which they use to insert their eggs into the host. Their wasp larvae develop within the host, consuming its tissues, which then results in its death. In some cases, the larvae of the butterfly will continue to grow and may even pupate before it succumbs to the parasitoid. Some parasitoids cause such high levels of mortality that they may be key factors in controlling the numbers of the butterfly population and are sometimes used in biological control.

The larvae of many tiny wasps develop within other insects. These are effectively parasites and are called 'parasitoids'. The wasp's larvae in this photograph were mature and were exiting the caterpillar before they pupated.

Some flies belonging to the family *Tachinidae* are also parasitoids of butterflies. These flies are very bristly and greyish in colour. Their eggs are generally laid on the larvae. These hatch and the tiny fly maggots tunnel into the caterpillar. Alternatively, the fly may oviposit on the larval food so that the caterpillar ingests them. The larvae of the fly then develop within the host and may cause high mortality.

Bacteria and viruses also attack butterflies. Their effects are most marked in the larvae. Here they cause a disease called 'wilting disease' or septicemia. The bacteria or virus attacks the walls of the gut, causing the tissue to break down. They can then cross the walls of the gut and invade other tissues. Other micro-organisms which usually remain harmless in the gut may also cross and attack body tissues. Larvae suffering from septicemia usually cease feeding, become very flaccid and may exude a mucous-filled fluid from the anus and/or head. Some bacterial strains are now being used as insecticides and as biological control agents.

How do butterflies protect themselves?

Protective mechanisms against predators are often very spectacular and include camouflage, disruptive colours, eye spots, warning colours, distastefulness, pungent and irritating odours, mimicry, behavioural traits, spines, and silken webs. Several species of butterflies have colours and shapes which make it difficult for predators to spot them. Some have warning colouring such as red combined with black and yellow.

Butterflies are often adorned with bright eye spots on their wings (see the Jamaican Satyra, the Buckeye and Cassius Blue). As predators often attempt to capture the butterfly by the body, these eye spots act as decoys from the true, less conspicuous head. They are useful, judging from the many bird beak and lizard mouth marks which may be observed on the wings. Some species combine eye spots with distastefulness so that, as the predator grabs at the spots on the wing, it releases its prey as it is distasteful. The butterfly escapes with a damaged wing, but its head is still in tact. In some cases the eye spots are large and give the illusion of being the eyes of a big animal, thus deterring the would-be predator. (See *Papilio homerus* larvae.)

Some butterflies contain toxic chemicals or substances which make them unpalatable. Such chemicals may be sequestered from the food plants, for example, the Variegated Fritillary which collects cyanide from the plant 'Ram Goat Dash Along' (*Turnera ulmifolia*). Some species manufacture toxins from chemicals they collect from plants, as do the Milkweed butterflies. Such species may have warning colours which the predators quickly learn to associate with unpalatability.

Unpalatable species may develop similar colours and so reinforce the effect on the predator, this is called 'Batesian mimicry'. In some cases a species that does not have toxins may have similar colours to a toxic species and so derive protection from its predator. This is known as 'Mullerian mimicry'.

Butterflies have developed many behavioural traits to protect themselves from predators:

a Those species relying upon camouflage are generally dispersed, while those with warning colours are often gregarious and so increase the impact of the colours.

b Larvae often feed at night when their predators are least active.

c Disturbed larvae may jerk their bodies, often in a snake-like fashion.

d Some species have markings on their thorax mirroring the heads of lizards and snakes. They also have osmeteria – reversible fleshy tentacles in their thorax, just behind the head. These may be brightly coloured and startle the predator when protruded. Moreover, they may also simultaneously release a pungent odour.

e Protection against parasites and pathogens include antibodies, phagocytes and encapsulation of the invading organisms.

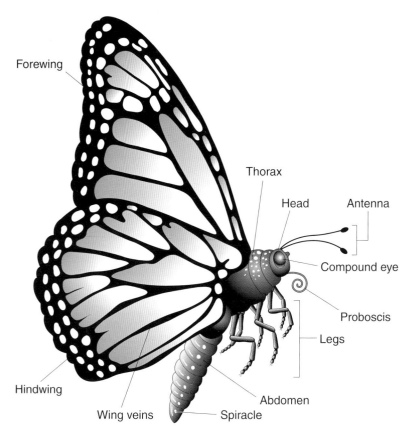

Forewing

Thorax

Head

Antenna

Compound eye

Proboscis

Legs

Hindwing

Wing veins

Abdomen

Spiracle

Anatomy of a butterfly

Moths and Butterflies (Order: Lepidoptera)

Over 125 000 species of moths and butterflies have been described to date, of which about 12 000 are butterflies. Many more remain undiscovered and some will become extinct before they are ever recognised.

It is sometimes difficult to distinguish between a butterfly and a moth. Some differences need close, detailed examination, but useful differentiating features include:

1 The antennae of butterflies are always club-shaped, although they may be hooked. They are never feathery or thread-like. The antennae of moths, however, may be thread-like, feathery but never club-shaped.

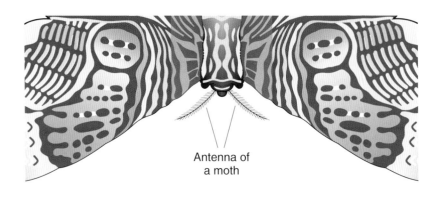

Antenna of
a moth

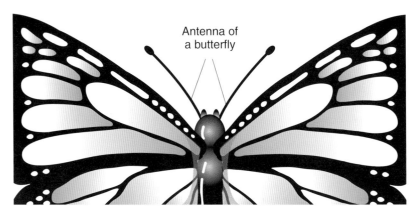

Antenna of
a butterfly

The antennae of a butterfly and a moth

2 Moths have a structure called the 'frenulum', which is used to couple the fore and hind wings. This is a bristle located near the base of the hind wing and held tightly by a hook called the 'reticulum' on the fore wing. (It might be necessary to remove some scales before this structure can be seen.) This structure allows the wings to operate as a single unit resulting in more efficient flight. In butterflies the same is achieved by overlapping the wings.

3 Butterflies are generally active during the day and moths by night. However, there are some moths which fly during the day, and these are often coloured like butterflies. A good example is *Uranus sloanus* (Uranidae) which is not only brightly-coloured but also has tails and may be mistaken for a swallowtail butterfly. It is endemic to Jamaica and is the most beautiful member of the genus. It has not been recorded for several decades, however, and is perhaps extinct. *Utetheisa ornatrix* (Arctiidae) and *Uthethesia bella* are other common day-flying moths.

Uranus sp.

Uthethesia bella

Because moths generally sit on vegetation during the day, their colours are often protective. Many have very cryptic colours allowing them to blend into the background, or they may alter their shape, making it difficult for predators to spot them.

On Jamaica, the number of species of moths far exceeds that of the butterflies. They also have a much wider range of sizes. The largest moth in Jamaica is the giant Black Witch (*Ascalapha odora*) with a wing span of 6 ins (15 cm) which is about the same size as the largest butterfly, the Giant Swallowtail. However, while the smallest butterfly, the Pygmy Blue, has a wingspan of 3/5 in (1.5 cm) the smallest moths are tiny, 1/12 in (2 mm) and hence are called the micro-lepidoptera.

Moths are called 'bats' on Jamaica, not to be confused with the mammalian bats which are called 'rat bats'. Some 'bats' are believed to be the spirits of ancestors and are often feared. Butterflies are seen as good spirits in some cultures and are often depicted as angels. Angels are sometimes adorned with butterfly wings.

The Black Witch Moth or 'Duppy Bat' (*Aescalapha odorata*) is a common moth that is believed to contain the spirits of ancestors.

Butterflies of Jamaica

To date, 134 species of butterflies, belonging to eight families have been described from Jamaica – 20 of these are endemic species and 23 are endemic subspecies. Both the largest and the smallest butterflies in the New World occur on Jamaica. They are, respectively, the Giant Swallowtail (*Papilio homerus*) and the Pygmy Blue (*Brephidium exilis*). Some species occur in very high numbers while others are very rare. One species, the Giant Swallowtail, is listed as endangered and one, the Blue Swallowtail, as threatened/vulnerable.

Butterflies occur in all Jamaica's geographical zones, from the incredibly wet John Crow Mountains to the dry cactus scrub of the south coast; from the shaded forests of Blue Mountain Peak to the open, salt-sprayed herbs of the seashore.

Some species have very restricted distributions, while others utilise a wide variety of habitats. The Pygmy Blue is found in the salt marsh-like areas close to the sea, while the American Painted Lady and the Dainty Sulphur generally occur in clearings at altitudes over 4000 ft (1200 m). The Jamaican Patch is found only in cleared areas of the Cockpit Country, while the Zebra occurs in shady areas at all altitudes. The Lignum vitae butterfly swarms through the streets of Kingston, while the Clear Wing hides in the shady areas of the moist forests.

For the butterfly enthusiast there is always something of interest on Jamaica.

The Butterflies

Opposite: Dirce (*Colobura dirce avinoffi*)

◆ DANAIDAE
The Milkweed butterflies

The *Danaidae* are called the Milkweed butterflies as their larvae feed on plants of the family *Asclepiaceae* (*e.g.* Red Head (*Asclepias curassavica*)) which have a milky sap. The larvae sequester poisons from the plants and these are used for protection against predators. The poisons, which are passed on to the pupae and adults, include cardiac glycosides, which cause nausea and even death to the would-be predator. Danaids are famous for their migration in order to avoid winters and have been recorded migrating from Canada to Mexico. The population on Jamaica does not migrate. Four species have been recorded from Jamaica. For the beginner, some species are difficult to distinguish on the wing.

Monarch
Danaus plexippus (Linnaeus)
Wingspan: 3³/₄in (9.5 cm)

This is the largest of the Milkweed butterflies on Jamaica. It is easily recognisable by its deep rich colouring and the broad, black band running along the rear margins of the hind wing.

Eresimus
Danaus eresimus eresimus (Cramer)
Wingspan: 3¹/₄in (8.5 cm)

Monarch (*Danaus plexippus*) (dorsal)

Monarch (*Danaus plexippus*) (ventral)

Eresimus (*Danaus eresimus eresimus*)

♦ **DANAIDAE**

Gilippus
Danaus gilippus jamaicensis
(Bates)
Wingspan: 3 in (7.5 cm)

These two species are very similar but *Danaus eresimus* is larger, deep brown and has yellow spots on the under side of the hind wing. The smaller *Danaus gilippus* is greyish brown and does not have the yellow spots. *Danaus cleophile*, the smallest Danaid on Jamaica, has a black band running along the rear margin of the fore wing, as has *D. gilippus*. However, this species is extremely rare and only a few specimens have been collected to date.

Gilippus
(*Danaus gilippus jamaicensis*) (dorsal)

Gilippus
(*Danaus gilippus jamaicensis*) (ventral)

◆ NYMPHALIDAE

The Nymphalids

A family with a tremendous variation in size, colour and habits, the Nymphalids are easily recognised by their under-developed foreleg. Over 6000 species have been described world-wide of which 29 are known to occur on Jamaica.

White Peacock
Anartia jatrophae Moschler
Wingspan: 1¼ins (4.5cm)

A prevalent butterfly, common among shrubs of disturbed areas, the White Peacock often settles with its wings open. The species is widely distributed in the Caribbean but there is a Jamaican subspecies, *Anartia jatrophae jamaicensis.*

American Painted Lady
Vanessa virginensis (Drury)
Wingspan: 2ins (5cm)

The Jamaican population of the American Painted Lady is generally found in the mountains above 3300ft (1000m) and is often seen along the road as one hikes to Blue Mountain Peak and Cinchona Gardens. Ventrally, the hind wing has two large black-ringed, blue-eyed spots. This species is widespread in the Americas.

White Peacock
(*Anartia jatrophae*)

American Painted
Lady (*Vanessa
virginensis*) (dorsal)

American Painted
Lady (*Vanessa
virginensis*) (ventral)

Malachite
Siproeta stelenes stelenes
(Linnaeus)
Wingspan: 3½ins (9cm)

This slow-flying butterfly likes shrubby areas next to forests. It is not shy and may be picked up with the fingers from leaves or while it feeds on rotting fruit. In flight, it can be mistaken for the Zebra as they are of similar colour and both have a slow flight pattern. The Malachite is easily damaged and looses its scales quickly. Its colour changes from intense green to yellow-green. The wings are translucent and the sunlight shining through them produces a most dramatic effect. The Malachite is widespread, from southern USA to Brazil.

Zebra
Heliconius charitonius
simulator Rober
Wingspan: 3ins (8cm)

This is a widespread species, which prefers to fly lazily in open forests. Members of the group are famous for being distasteful and for their pungency – two characteristics offering protection from predators. The larvae sequester the chemicals used from the food plants – several species of *Passiflora* (passion fruit family). At night or in overcast weather, dozens of butterflies congregate upside down on twigs. This species is widespread throughout the Americas.

Malachite (*Siproeta stelenes stelenes*) (dorsal)

Malachite (*Siproeta stelenes stelenes*) (ventral)

Zebra (*Heliconius charitonius simulator*) (dorsal)

◆ NYMPHALIDAE

Antillean Dagger Tail
Marpesia eleuchea pellenis
(Godart)
Wingspan: 2½ins (6.5cm)

This species is easily distinguished by its long, slender extensions to the hind wing in the shape of a dagger. Generally an uncommon butterfly, the Antillean Dagger Tail might be found in abundance feeding in sunlit areas in some localities. The species occurs throughout The Bahamas and the Greater Antilles.

Zebra (*Heliconius charitonius simulator*) (ventral)

Antillean Dagger Tail (*Marpesia eleuchea pellenis*) (dorsal)

Antillean Dagger Tail (*Marpesia eleuchea pellenis*) (ventral)

Dirce
Colobura dirce avinoffi
Comstock
Wingspan: 2³/₄ins (7 cm)

Dirce sits head down, wings closed, on the trunks of trees (especially fruit trees). It makes short darting flights when disturbed and often returns to the same trunk. With wings closed, the markings on the under side of its wings break up the shape of the butterfly making them difficult to see. Moreover, the markings on the rear tip of the hind wings create the appearance of a head to both the potential predator and the inexperienced collector. Dirce occurs from the Greater Antilles and South America.

Jamaican Admiral
Adelpha abyla (Hewitson)
Wingspan: 2–2¹/₄ins (5–6 cm.)

The Jamaican Admiral is easily distinguished in flight by the blue 'V'-shaped bands running across the wings. It frequents open glades near forested areas. It may glide playfully from sunlight to shady areas, but is a strong flyer. This is an endemic species.

Dirce (*Colobura dirce avinoffi*) (dorsal)

Dirce (*Colobura dirce avinoffi*) (ventral)

Jamaican Admiral (*Adelpha abyla*)

Jamaican Dynamine
Dynamine egaea egaea
(Fabricius)
Wingspan: 1¹/₂ins (4cm)

The upper sides of the wings differ according to whether the butterfly is male or female. Those of the male are metallic green, whereas those of the female have metallic blue inner areas with a white midline and the outer areas are black. This lowland species prefers dry areas. It also occurs in Cuba, Hispaniola and from Colombia to Mexico.

Jamaican Dynamine
(*Dynamine egaea
egaea*) (female,
dorsal)

Jamaican Dynamine
(*Dynamine egaea
egaea*) (female,
ventral)

Jamaican Dynamine
(*Dynamine egaea
egaea*) (male, dorsal)

Orion
Historis odius odius (Fabricius)
Wingspan: 4$\frac{1}{2}$–5 ins (11–13 cm)

Cadmus
Historis acheronta cadmus
(Cramer)
Wingspan: 3$\frac{1}{2}$–4 ins (9–10 cm)

Orion and Cadmus are large-bodied quick-flying butterflies. The two species are quite similar in appearance but Orion is bigger, lighter in colour, and has a single white spot towards the apex of the upper side of the fore wing. Cadmus, on the other hand, has a row of white spots near the apex of the

Orion *(Historis odius odius)* (dorsal)

Orion *(Historis odius odius)* (ventral, feeding on plant sap alongside flower beetles)

Cadmus (*Historis acheronta cadmus*) (dorsal)

fore wing. When at rest, the wings of both species are tightly closed and resemble dried leaves. These butterflies frequent ripe and fermenting fruits. Orion is more common than Cadmus but both may occur together. Widespread in distribution, Cadmus prevails in the Greater Antilles and Orion in both the Greater and Lesser Antilles.

Jamaican Goatweed Butterfly
Anaea portia Fabricius
Wingspan: 2³/₄–3 ins (7–8 cm)

The Jamaican Goatweed Butterfly is a forest butterfly with a preference for dry forests. It often sits on twigs with little leaves and, with wings closed, it resembles a dried leaf. The bright upper side is displayed when it is disturbed or may be seen as it dashes off at high speed. The sexes are similar but the female has black irregular lines across the upper surface of the wings. The Jamaican Goatweed Butterfly may be confused with *Memphis (Anaea) johnsoni*. However, *M. johnsoni* is lighter in colour, has a distinct, light-coloured patch towards the apex of the upper side of the fore wing and is smaller, having a wingspan of 2¼ins (6 cm). It is an uncommon species in Jamaica but is widely distributed in the Americas. It occurs generally in dry forested areas.

Cadmus (*Historis acheronta cadmus*) (ventral)

Jamaican Goatweed Butterfly (*Anaea troglodyta*) (dorsal)

Jamaican Goatweed Butterfly (*Anaea troglodyta*) (ventral)

Jamaican Mestra, Dorcas
Mestra dorcas Fabricius
Wingspan: 1¼ins (4 cm)

A common butterfly in the lowlands throughout Jamaica, the Jamaican Mestra flies slowly among the grass and shrubs. It is delicate and is not shy. The larvae feed on *Tragia volubilis* (cow-itch). This is an endemic species.

Variegated Fritillary
Euptoieta claudia claudia
(Cramer)
Wingspan: 2¼ins (6 cm)

Jamaican Mestra,
Dorcas (*Mestra dorcas*)

Variegated Fritillary
(*Euptoieta claudia
claudia*) (dorsal)

Variegated Fritillary
(*Euptoieta claudia
claudia*) (ventral)

◆ NYMPHALIDAE

Tropical Fritillary
Euptoieta hegesia hegesia
(Cramer)
Wingspan: 2¹/₄ins (6 cm)

These two species are similar but the ground colour of the Variegated Fritillary is darker than that of the Tropical Fritillary and the black spots of the upper side of the wings of the former look more like eye spots. Both are fairly common in open lowland areas.

The Variegated Fritillary oviposits on several groups of plants including *Viola, Passiflora* and *Desmodium.* The Tropical Fritillary oviposits on *Turnera ulmifolia* and *Passiflora.* The caterpillars sequester cyanide from the food plants. Both species occur from southern USA to Argentina.

Buckeye
Junonia (Precis) genoveva
(Cramer)
Wingspan: 2¹/₄ins (6 cm)

Tropical Fritillary
(*Euptoieta hegesia
hegesia*) (dorsal)

Tropical Fritillary
(*Euptoieta hegesia
hegesia*) (ventral)

Buckeye, Genoveva
(*Junonia (Precis)
genoveva*) (dorsal)

Junonia (Precis) evarete (Stoll)
Wingspan: 2¹/₄ins (6 cm)

These two species may be difficult to distinguish on the wing. However, *Junonia genoveva* has a white band on its fore wing which is shaded with orange and the under surface of the hind wing is a rich brown with three distinct eye spots. *J. evarete* has a white band on the fore wing, which is distinct, and has little or no orange shading and the under side of the fore wing is a dirty brown with two small eye spots.

J. evarete prefers shorelines and mangroves, while *J. genoveva* is found in open fields at varying altitudes. Both species have a wide distribution – from southern USA to northern South America.

Buckeye, Genoveva
(*Junonia (Precis)
genoveva*) (ventral)

Buckeye, Evarete
(*Junonia (Precis)
evarete*) (dorsal)

Buckeye, Evarete
(*Junonia (Precis)
evarete*) (ventral)

Jamaican Crescent Spot
Antillea (Phyciodes) proclea
(Doubleday and Hewitson)
Wingspan: 1 in (2.5 cm)

This is a checkered orange and black species with a small white spot on the apex of the upper side of the fore wing and five small eye spots on the under side of the hind wing. The Jamaican Crescent Spot is a common species along the forest edge and in cleared areas up to an altitude of 20 ft (600 m). It is an endemic species.

Cuban Crescent Spot
Anthanassa (Phyciodes) frisia
Poey
Wingspan: 1¼ ins (3 cm)

This butterfly closely resembles the Jamaican Crescent Spot and is difficult to differentiate in flight. However, the Cuban lacks the white spot on the under side of the fore wing and the five eye spots on the under side of the hind wing. This is a widespread species in the Greater Antilles and southern USA.

Jamaican Crescent
Spot (*Antillea*
(Phyciodes) proclea)

Cuban Crescent Spot
(Anthanassa
(Phyciodes) frisia
(dorsal)

Cuban Crescent Spot
(Anthanassa
(Phyciodes) frisia
(ventral)

◆ NYMPHALIDAE

Julia
Dryas iulia delila (Fabricius)
Wingspan: 3 ins (8 cm)

This brightly coloured butterfly is common throughout Jamaica. It is a swift flyer and is often seen feeding in domestic gardens. At rest, it sits with its wings closed, the paler colours of the underside appearing as a dried leaf. When disturbed, the wings open to give a startling bright orange-red flash as the butterfly dashes off. Females generally have more prominent black areas on both wings. Julia is widely distributed in the Americas and West Indies.

Tropical Silverspot
Agraulis (Dione) vanillae insularis Linnaeus
Wingspan: 2¹/₄ ins (6 cm)

The Tropical Silverspot is a widespread butterfly which frequents gardens. It is a fast flyer when disturbed, the silver of the under wings flashing as it goes. In flight, the species is easily distinguishable from Julia by the bright silver on the under wings and the black spots on the upper side. The larvae feed on several species of *Passiflora*. This species occurs from southern North America, through the Caribbean to South America.

Julia (*Dryas iulia delila*)

Tropical Silverspot *(Agraulis (Dione) vanillae insularis)* (dorsal)

Tropical Silverspot *(Agraulis (Dione) vanillae insularis)* (ventral)

Jamaican Patch
Atlantea pantoni (Kaye)
Wingspan: 2¼ins (6cm)

This endemic species is restricted to the Cockpit Country, where it may be locally common. Its preferred habitat is open areas where it may be seen feeding and basking on low vegetation. The sexes are distinct. Males have a complex pattern of black or black-brown, with many patches of orange-brown. In the female the black pattern is similar to that of the male but the orange-brown is replaced by yellow to creamy-white except on those just inside the margin of the hind wing which are brick red. The underside of the fore-wing is coloured similar to the upper surface in the respective sexes and the hind wing in both cases is much like that of the upper wing of the female, the yellow patches sometimes being lighter.

Jamaican Patch
(*Atlantea pantoni*)
(male, dorsal)

Jamaican Patch
(*Atlantea pantoni*)
(male, ventral)

Jamaican Patch
(*Atlantea pantoni*)
(female, dorsal)

◆ LYCAENIDAE

Blues and Hairstreaks

These are small, delicate butterflies which are often blue or green. The Blues, as the name suggests, are dominated by refractory scales (see page 4). There are five species on Jamaica, two of which are endemic. The hairstreaks, which are generally brown with some blue and green, have one or two hair-like tails on the hind wings. Twelve species of hairstreaks occur on Jamaica.

Lycaenids have interesting life histories. In some cases, the larvae secrete a sweet substance, called 'honeydew', which attracts ants who visit and tend the larvae for it.

Cassius Blue
Leptotes cassius theonus
(Lucas)
Wingspan: 1 in (2.5 cm)

The male Cassius Blue is violet-blue on the upper side, while the female has spots and markings of brown on blue and white, the white being dominant on the hind wings. This is the most common blue on Jamaica and is found throughout the island, especially on the lowlands. This species has a wide distribution, from Texas to Argentina.

Hanno Blue
Hemiargus hanno ceraunus
(Fabricius)
Wingspan: 3/4 in (2 cm)

This common, widespread species is found in both dry and wet areas, but loves sunlight. The upper side of the male is a violet blue, while the female is dark brown with a distinct blue area at the base of the fore wing. It occurs from southern USA to South America.

Cassius Blue (*Leptotes cassius theonus*)

Cassius Blue (*Leptotes cassius theonus*)

Hanno Blue (*Hemiargus hanno ceraunus*) (female, dorsal)

Pygmy Blue
Brephidium exilis isophthalma
(Herrich-Schaffer)
Wingspan: 3/4 in (1.5 cm)

This is the smallest butterfly in the Americas and, perhaps, in the world. The upper surface is dark brown with a hint of copper – there might be a hint of blue at the base of the wing. It occurs in large numbers in fields of freshly planted *Sesuvium portulacastrum* (seaside purslane) and *Battis maritima* (Jamaican samphire) in saline marsh-like areas near to the sea. The species occurs from southern USA to South America.

Hanno Blue
(*Hemiargus hanno ceraunus*) (female, ventral)

Hanno Blue
(*Hemiargus hanno ceraunus*) (male, dorsal)

Pygmy Blue
(*Brephidium exilis isophthalma*)

◆ LYCAENIDAE

Gosse's Hairstreak
Strymon acis gossei (Comstock and Huntington)
Wingspan: $1/2$in (1.5 cm)

This species is easily recognised by the white bands across the under side of its wings. The upper side is dark brown. While most common along the sea coast, Gosse's Hairstreak also occurs in interior dry limestone areas, for example Long Mountain, and occasionally in areas such as the lower slopes of the Blue Mountains. It is an endemic subspecies.

Hewitson's Hairstreak
Strymon columella cybira (Hewitson)
Wingspan: 1 in (2.5 cm)

Hewitson's Hairstreak is quite abundant and widely distributed on Jamaica. The spots on the upper side of the hind wing easily distinguish this dark brown hairstreak. The female has a broad blue band on the hind wing. It is a rapid flyer but sits on low vegetation in open areas. It occurs in southern USA, central and northern South America and the Caribbean.

Gosse's Hairstreak
(*Strymon acis gossei*)

Hewitson's Hairstreak
(*Strymon columella
cybira*) (dorsal)

Hewitson's Hairstreak
(*Strymon columella
cybira*) (ventral)

Drury's Hairstreak
Electrostrymon (Strymon) pan
(Drury)
Wingspan: 1¼ins (3cm)

Drury's Hairstreak is common in high rainfall areas such as the John Crow Mountains and the Blue Mountains. It basks in the sun at the edge of clearings about 9ft (2m) above the ground. In the Rio Grande Valley it often sits on Cacoon vines. Both the upper and lower wing surfaces are dark brown, but the lower is of a lighter hue. It is an endemic species.

Panton's Hairstreak
Electrostrymon angelia pantoni
(Comstock and Huntington)
Wingspan: 1in (2.5cm)

The Panton's Hairstreak is fairly common and widely distributed on Jamaica. It sits on plants about 9ft (2m) above the ground and generally flies short distances. It is easily recognisable by the two tails on the hind wing, the hind tail being longer. It also has a distinct orange spot with a black dot between the tails, which is clearly visible as the butterfly sits with its wings folded. The upper surface of the wings of both sexes is dark brown, but the male has a large yellowish-brown area. It is an endemic subspecies.

Drury's Hairstreak
(*Electrostrymon
(Strymon) pan*)

Panton's Hairstreak
(*Electrostrymon
angelia pantoni*)

◆ PIERIDAE

Whites and Sulphurs

These are the most common butterflies on Jamaica. They are white, cream, yellow or orange, and are decorated with black markings and spots. There is a great variation in size – the smallest being the *Eurema* with a wingspan of 1¼ins (3 cm) and the largest, the *Anteos*, with a wingspan of 4 ins (10 cm).

Lignum vitae Butterfly
Kricogonia lyside (Godart)
Wingspan: 1¼ins (4.5 cm)

The Lignum vitae butterfly is a widespread species on Jamaica. The larvae feed on the *Lignum vitae* tree (*Guaiacum officinale*) and adults may be seen ovipositing on the leaves and feeding on the flowers. Occasionally, numbers become so great that swarms may be seen around the trees, while many migrating adults are hit by vehicles. When the *Lignum vitae* trees occur in recreational areas and private gardens the large number of larvae produced become a nuisance. *Kricogonia lyside* occurs from southern USA to northern South America.

Antillean Great White (Cabbage Butterfly)
Ascia monuste eubotea Godart
Wingspan: 2¼ins (6 cm)

Ascia monuste is a common butterfly, which may swarm after the rains of May/June and October/November. The upper surface of the wings is chalky-white with black markings at the margins (with smoky areas extending inwards). The amount of black varies greatly, and is generally significantly more in the females. The larvae feed on members of the *Crucifer* family (*e.g.* cabbage, radish, mustard), hence its common name, and they may become a pest. It also occurs in large numbers on the weed *Cleome gynandra*.

Lignum vitae Butterfly
(*Kricogonia lyside*)
(dorsal)

Lignum vitae Butterfly
(*Kricogonia lyside*)
(swarming on a
Lignum Vitae tree)

Antillean Great White
(*Ascia monuste
eubotea*) (Cabbage
butterfly)

◆ PIERIDAE

Josephina
Ascia (Ganyra) josephina paramaryllis Comstock
Wingspan: over 3 ins (8 cm)

The second species of *Ascia, A. josephina*, is larger than *A. monuste* and is all white except for a small dark spot on both sides of the fore wings. This is an uncommon species on Jamaica. Both species occur in southern USA, some Caribbean islands and south to Argentina. *A. monuste*, however, is the more widespread of the two.

Jamaican Albatross
Appias drusilla castalia Fabricius
Wingspan: 2¼ ins (6 cm)

The Jamaican Albatross is a common, white butterfly with somewhat pointed fore wings. There is a diffuse yellow colouring at the base of the wings (brighter on the under side) which is more marked in the females. The flight pattern is generally rapid and the species frequents open ground. *Appias drusilla* occurs from southern USA to southern Brazil.

Josephina (*Ascia josephina paramaryllis*)

Jamaican Albatross (*Appias drusilla castalia*) (dorsal)

Jamaican Albatross (*Appias drusilla castalia*) (puddling by a stream)

Dainty Sulphur
Nathalis iole Boisduval
Wingspan: ³/₄in (2cm)

The fore wing of this yellow butterfly has a wide black mark at its tip and a diffuse black bar across the bottom. The hind wing has a diffuse black bar across the top and small dark areas at the edge. The under side is marked with black, with a bit of orange. It is a weak flyer in open places and is more common at higher altitudes (above 4000ft (1200m). This species occurs from Central America to Canada.

Small Sulphurs
Eurema species

Small Sulphurs, generally not more than ³/₄–1¹/₄ in (2–3cm) in wingspan are common on Jamaica. Only one of the eleven species is endemic. The species are difficult to distinguish and this is made more difficult by extensive colour polymorphism. Some examples are given here but identifying specimens might necessitate consultation of a more detailed book such as Brown and Heineman (1972) or Smith *et al* (1994).

Dainty Sulphur
(*Nathalis iole*)

Eurema lisa euterpe
(dorsal)

Eurema lisa euterpe
(ventral)

♦ **PIERIDAE**

Eurema nise (ventral)
E.nise may be
mistaken for *E. lisa*
but it does not have
the orange spot on
the underside of the
hind wing. The species
shows great
polymorphism

Eurema nicippe
(ventral)

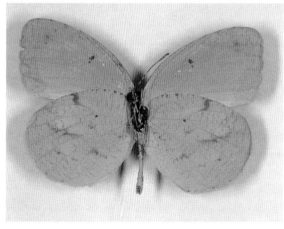

Eurema nicippe
(dorsal)

◆ PIERIDAE

Eurema daira palmira
(male, dorsal)

Eurema daira palmira
(male, ventral)

Eurema elathea
(male, dorsal)

♦ **PIERIDAE**

Eurema elathea
(male, ventral)

*Eurema proterpia
proterpia* (dorsal)

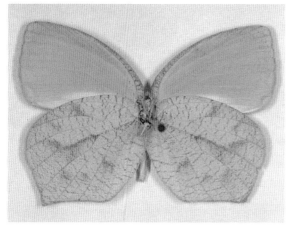

*Eurema proterpia
proterpia* (ventral)

Cloudless Sulphur
Phoebis sennae (Linnaeus)
Wingspan: 2¹/₄ins (6cm)

The male Cloudless Sulphur is pure yellow on the upper side, while the female has a black/brown fringe on the outer margin of both wings. The under sides are yellow with white spots in the centre of each wing. This is a common species in all parishes of Jamaica and has been recorded in large numbers, even offshore. The larvae feed on the leaves of *Cassia* species, especially *Cassia occidentalis*. It occurs from southern North America to Argentina.

Eurema nicippe
(ventral)

Cloudless Sulphur
(*Phoebis sennae*)
(male, ventral)

Cloudless Sulphur
(*Phoebis sennae*)
(female, ventral)

Orange Sulphurs
Phoebis agarithe antillea
Brown

Phoebis agarithe
antillia (dorsal)

Phoebis agarithe
antillia (ventral)

Phoebis argante Avinoff

These are the only two large orange butterflies on Jamaica. The upper sides of the wings of both species are similar and they are difficult to distinguish in flight. However, on the underside of the fore wing of *Phoebis agarithe antillia* there is a straight dark band running diagonally, while in *P. argante* the diagonal line is broken and somewhat crooked. Both species are widely distributed and are common on Jamaica. They generally sit with wings closed on the underside of leaves. *P. argarithe antillia* oviposits on the leaves of *Pithecolobium* (Privet, 'Bread-and-Cheese'), while *P. argante* oviposits on *Igna vera* (Panchock, River Koko). With a wingspan of 2½ins (6.5 cm), *P. argante* is slightly the bigger of the two. *P. argante* occurs in Central America, the West Indies and in northern regions of South America, while *P. agarithe antillia* occurs from southern North America, through the Caribbean to central South America.

Maerula
Anteos maerula maerula
(Fabricius)
Wingspan: 3½ins (9 cm)

This large, lemon-coloured butterfly cannot be confused with the other Pierids on Jamaica. It is a fast flyer and, when at rest, settles under a leaf with wings tightly closed so that it resembles a pale-green leaf. The wings are leathery. *Anteos maerula* has a wide distribution on Jamaica. It occurs from southern North America to Peru.

Phoebis argante

Maerula (*Anteos maerula maerula*) (dorsal)

Statira
Aphrissa statira cubana
d'Almeida
Wingspan: 2¹/₄ins (6 cm)

Hartonia
Aphrissa godartiana hartonia
Butler
Wingspan: 2³/₄ins (7 cm)

These two species closely resemble each other and close examination is necessary for identification. One distinguishing feature is the shape of the fore margin of the fore wing, which is curved in *Aphrissa hartonia* but straight in *A. statira*. However, they are rapid flyers and this cannot be observed on the wing. Females are generally more yellow than the males. *A. statira* was introduced from Cuba and now occurs throughout the island. *A. hartonia* is endemic and restricted to the Cockpit Country.

Maerula (*Anteos maerula maerula*) (ventral)

Statira (*Aphrissa statira cubana*)

◆ PAPILIONIDAE

The Swallowtails

The Swallowtails are by far Jamaica's most well known family of butterflies, and include the largest individuals on the island. They are termed Swallowtails because of the tail-like extensions on the hind wings. There are seven species on Jamaica, four endemic species, and two endemic subspecies. This is a remarkable level of endemism within a single family.

Thersites
Papilio (Heraclides) thersites
Fabricius
Wingspan: 4³/₄ins (12 cm)

The male Thersites is unmistakable and may be seen as a large, bright yellow butterfly moving across the landscape. The female is black and may be distinguished from the Jamaican Polydamas and Pelaus by its large size and the distinct band of yellow on the outer margin of the hind wings. The males are seen more frequently than the females. It is a widespread, but uncommon, endemic species. The larvae feed on citrus and other rutaceous plants.

Cuban Swallowtail (Citrus Swallowtail)
Papilio (Heraclides) andraemon (Hubner)
Wingspan: 3³/₄ins (9 cm)

This is the most common of the swallowtails on Jamaica and is often seen in gardens and around citrus trees. It was introduced from Cuba in the mid-1940s. This species is easily recognisable because of the unbroken band of yellow across both fore and hind wings. The larvae, which are black and white and sometimes called 'orange dog' on Jamaica, feed on the leaves of citrus plants and may become a pest. It occurs in Cuba, The Bahamas and Cayman.

Thersites (*Papilio
(Heraclides) thersites*)
(male, dorsal)

Thersites (*Papilio
(Heraclides) thersites*)
(female, dorsal)

Cuban swallowtail
(*Papilio (Heraclides)
andraemon*)

◆ PAPILIONIDAE

Thoas
Papilio (Heraclides) thoas melonius (Rothschild and Jordan)
Wingspan: 4¹/₄ins (11 cm)

A beautiful, but uncommon butterfly, the Thoas, on the wing, is often mistaken for the Cuban Swallowtail. It is believed that numbers have decreased since the invasion by the Cuban Swallowtail, but the interaction between the two species has not been studied. The larvae of Thoas feed on citrus, and other rutaceous plants such as *Zanthoxylum*. Although the species is now rare, it still has a wide distribution. *Papilio thoas* occurs in Cuba, Central America and southern North America. *P. thoas melonius* is a Jamaican endemic subspecies.

Jamaican Polydamas
Battus polydamas jamaicensis (Rothschild and Jordan)
Wingspan: 3¹/₂ins (9 cm)

This is the tail-less swallowtail. It is a common species with a wide distribution. It is found in all habitats and frequents gardens. The Jamaican Polydamas is a rapid flyer but frequently stops to hover in front of flowers while it feeds. The adults oviposit on species of *Aristolochia* and *Passiflora*. It is sometimes confused with Pelaus but the yellow band on the fore wing runs parallel to the margin of the wing (see Pelaus, below). The yellow spots on the under side of the fore

Thoas (*Papilio (Heraclides) thoas melonius*)

Jamaican Polydamas (*Battus polydamas jamaicensis*) (ventral)

wing are similar to those on the upper side. The hind wing has irregular yellow spots on the margin and red spots on the inside of these. *Battus polydamas* is widely distributed throughout the Caribbean and America. *B. polydamas jamaicensis* is an endemic subspecies.

Pelaus
Papilio (Heraclides) pelaus pelaus Fabricius
Wingspan: 4 ins (10 cm)

Papilio pelaus pelaus is found most frequently in moist forests such as those of the John Crow Mountains. On the wing, it is sometimes confused with the Jamaican Polydamas, especially since the tails are easily lost and, even if present, are difficult to see in flight. It may easily be distinguished, however, as the light yellow band runs diagonally across the fore wing and not parallel to the margin as in the Jamaican Polydamas. It flies, sometimes lazily, in shady areas. When the weather becomes overcast, Pelaus sits, with wings open, no more than 3 ft (1 m) above the ground. This species occurs throughout the Greater Antilles.

Jamaican Polydamas
(*Battus polydamas jamaicensis*) (dorsal)

Pelaus (*Papilio (Heraclides) pelaus pelaus*)

Blue Swallowtail
*Eurytides (Graphium,
Protesilaus) marcellinus*
(Doubleday)
Wingspan: 2³/₄ins (7 cm)

This is the only blue swallowtail on Jamaica. Once abundant enough to swarm through Kingston, today, it is rare. A population occurs in the region of Rozelle in St Thomas, and smaller populations may be found in Western Jamaica. The larvae feed on Black Lancewood (*Oxandra lanceolata*). The adults are generally seen after the rains of May/June. The Blue Swallowtail is listed as vulnerable by the IUCN Red Data Book, but there is a great need for intensive studies on the status of the species. It is an endemic species.

Blue Swallowtail
(*Eurytides* (*Graphium, Protesilaus*)
marcellinus) (dorsal)

Blue Swallowtail
(*Eurytides* (*Graphium, Protesilaus*)
marcellinus) (ventral)

Jamaican Giant Swallowtail
Papilio (Pterourus) homerus
Fabricius
Wingspan: average: 6 ins
(15 cm); maximum 8 ins (20 cm)

'It was day five of our hike through the rainforest of the John Crow Mountains. Our guide was taking us along a path created by wild pigs. For days we had endured this strange weather of 'passing sunshine' not the customary passing showers experienced in Kingston. At 12:43 pm the Rio Grande Valley was bathed with sunlight and suddenly there were loud shouts of 'homerus! homerus!'

We gazed spellbound as Jamaica's largest butterfly, its wings playing in the sunshine, came floating along. One minute later it was gone. We who had come to take photographs stood in silence, cameras forgotten, but with the picture of that encounter indelibly engraved in our minds'. (extract from *'Papilio homerus'*, *Jamaica Naturalist*, Vol 3)

This extract describes the authors' first encounter with *Papilio homerus*. Such a response is not surprising, if one considers that *Papilio homerus* was regarded by its earlier admirers as the most 'noble' of butterflies. Indeed the butterfly's name, *homerus*, was inspired by comparison with the ancient Greek poet, Homer, whose epic works are considered a byword for all that is lofty, majestic and grand. The sight of *homerus* in its leisurely, playful flight in the midst of the tropical forests is indeed unforgettable.

Jamaica's Giant Swallowtail butterfly, *Papilio homerus*, is considered the largest of the true swallowtail species in the world. It is also the largest butterfly in the Americas. A few species of butterflies that occur in places such as Papua New Guinea and Malaysia are larger than *P. homerus* and these are so large that they are called birdwings. The largest of these is Queen Alexandra's Birdwing (*Ornithoptera alexandrae*) of Papua New Guinea, which achieves a wingspan of over 10 ins (25 cm).

P. homerus is confined to Jamaica where it once inhabited seven of the fourteen parishes. Today, it is found in only two isolated and diminishing strongholds: an eastern population in the parishes of St Thomas and Portland at the junction of the Blue and John Crow Mountain Ranges, and a western population in the rugged Cockpit Country of the parishes of Trelawny and St Elizabeth.

Jamaican Giant
Swallowtail (*Papilio
(Pterourus) homerus*)
basking in the sun.

Jamaican Giant
Swallowtail (*Papilio
(Pterourus) homerus*)
feeding

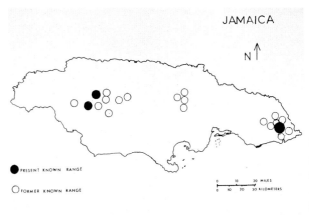

Map showing the
population
distribution of the
Jamaican Giant
Swallowtail (*Papilio
(Pterourus) homerus*)

Jamaica's Giant Swallowtail butterfly is endangered and is protected under the Jamaica Wild Life Act. It is therefore illegal to have this butterfly, or any part of it, in your possession (unless permission is given by the relevant authority (NEPA)). These restrictions also apply in any country that is a signatory to the Convention for International Trade on Endangered Species of Wild Fauna and Flora (CITES). The authors' study group of three, working for six hours a day over a five-day period in any one month, found such low numbers that in some months only a few eggs and caterpillars were recorded but no adults were ever seen. The highest number of *P. homerus* seen by the group was 48 (June, 1991), followed by 28 and 23 in June, 1991 and June, 1992 respectively.

While *P. homerus* is primarily a wet forest butterfly, it is not restricted to virgin forests. Breeding populations also occur in secondary forests as well as in areas where the forest has been cleared and is either being used for agriculture or has been abandoned, allowing the highly modified shrub-land to have become established. The population does well in the forested areas, but suffers high mortality in the cleared areas. This seems to be one of the key factors leading to the demise of this butterfly. The cleared parts of the habitats, therefore, are like 'sinks' or 'black holes' that are unable to sustain their own populations and thus the future of the butterfly depends upon adults migrating from the forested area.

The high mortality rate is caused mainly by parasitic wasps attacking the eggs and, to a lesser extent, bacteria attacking the larvae. It is not clear why these wasps do so well when the forests are cleared, but their impact will become even more marked as the forests shrink and the 'sinks' or 'black holes' get bigger. Survival of the species might ultimately depend on the establishment, or maintenance, of a proper balance between the forested and cleared areas in the butterfly's habitat.

Further pressure is placed on the population by illegal collecting/ poaching of adults for the international butterfly trade. Legal collecting, however, becomes important as population numbers fall to low levels.

The life cycle of *P. homerus* is very interesting, as the caterpillar goes through a series of remarkable changes and possesses an array of defensive mechanisms against predators. In the early stages, it is black and white and resembles the droppings of lizards and birds.

In addition, the thorax of these stages is also equipped with masses of sharp spines and tubercles. The older caterpillar is predominantly green in colour and blends well into the green, leafy background, while the brown markings on its sides give it the appearance of a dried, curled leaf.

From the front, the markings on the enlarged thorax create a snake-

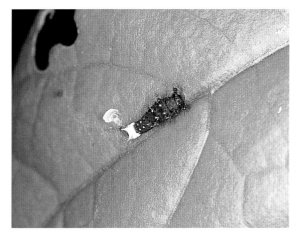

Early larvae of the Jamaican Giant Swallowtail (*Papilio (Pterourus) homerus*) resembling lizard/bird dropping

Late larvae of the Jamaican Giant Swallowtail (*Papilio (Pterourus) homerus*)

Jamaican Giant Swallowtail (*Papilio (Pterourus) homerus*) resting on a rainy day, resembling a dried leaf

like appearance. When disturbed, the larva will raise its anterior end and move in a snake-like manner.

The next line of defense is a pair of osmeteria. In the early stages, the osmeteria are small and brown, but in the later stages they are long, brick red and look like a snake's tongue. They shoot out rapidly when it is abruptly or violently disturbed. The predator is thus confronted by what looks like a snake: large eyes, very large mouth, a long, forked, red tongue and a body swaying back and forth as though about to strike. A musty terpenoid scent which it emits acts as a further deterrent.

The mature larva is very large and reaches a length of 2¾ins (7 cm). The pupa is generally woody-brown in colour, with black and white blotches and is thus very difficult to see as it looks like dried, curled leaves or other plant debris.

The larvae feed on the leaves of two plants belonging to the genus *Hernandia* (one species in the west and the other in the east). Both plants are found only on Jamaica. The adults, however, collect nectar from flowers of a wide variety of colours, shapes and sizes. Some favourite plants include Sage (*Lantana camara*), Shoe Black Hibiscus (*Hibiscus rosa-sinensis*), Black Stick (*Urena lobata*) and cacoon (*Entada gigas*).

P. homerus is Jamaica's most famous butterfly and, while it has not been formally designated Jamaica's National Butterfly, it is regarded as such and is being used more and more as a national symbol. It is now a familiar sight on postage stamps, telephone cards, credit cards, bumper stickers, T-Shirts and is included in the logo of the Blue and John Crow Mountains National Park and the J$1000.00 bank note.

Many people often mistakenly report sightings of *P. homerus*, when, in fact, it is another swallowtail such as *P. andraemon* or *P. thersites*. Unless you have visited the heart of the Cockpit Country or the John Crow Mountains, the chances are, you have not seen the Giant Swallowtail ... not alive, at least!

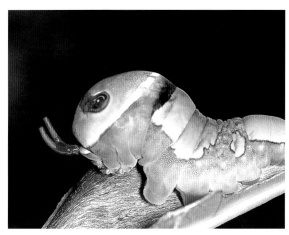

Late larvae of the
Jamaican Giant
Swallowtail (*Papilio
(Pterourus) homerus*)
osmeteria extruded
and behaving like a
snake when disturbed

◆ HESPERIDAE

The Skippers

The skippers are so named because their flight pattern is rapid and they seem to dart or skip from place to place. They are generally heavy bodied and may be recognised by their hooked antennae (see p. 10). Some forty species, four of which are endemic, have been recorded from Jamaica. Nine subspecies have also been recorded.

Butler's Jamaican Skipper
Astraptes jaira (Butler)
Wingspan: 2 ins (5 cm)

Butler's Jamaica Skipper is a widely-distributed, endemic species, which often sits on leaves, with wings open, basking in the early morning sun, or on the under side of leaves during the heat of the day.

Roy's Skipper
Astraptes anaphus anausis
(Goodman and Salvin)
Wingspan: 2 ins (5 cm)

This dark brown skipper is probably restricted to the eastern end of the island and is common in the foothills of the John Crow Mountains, *e.g.* in the Rio Grande Valley and Bath. It flies mainly in open areas. Roy's Skipper occurs throughout the West Indies.

Checkered Skipper
Pyrgus oileus (Linnaeus)
Wingspan: 1¹/₄ in (3 cm)

This common skipper, with its distinct checkered colouring, may be seen darting from place to place in open areas, The markings on the under and upper sides of the wings are similar. It occurs from southern USA to South America.

Butler's Jamaica Skipper (*Astraptes jaira*)

Roy's skipper (*Astraptes anaphus anausis*)

Checkered Skipper (*Pyrgus oileus*)

Church's Jamaican Skipper
Chioides catillus churchi Bell and Comstock
Wingspan: 2 ins (5 cm)

Common Tailed Skipper
Urbanus proteus (Linnaeus)
Wingspan: 2 ins (5 cm)

These two skippers both have long tails. The latter is much more common, but both are widely distributed on Jamaica. The species may be differentiated because Church's Jamaican Skipper is dark brown with yellow spots on the fore wing. The Common Skipper, meanwhile, has white spots on the fore wing and shiny green or blue colouring at the base of the upper side of the wings. Church's Jamaican Skipper is an endemic subspecies, while the Common Tailed Skipper is widely distributed throughout the Caribbean.

Evan's Jamaican Skipper
Polygonus leo hagar Evans
Wingspan: 2 ins (5 cm)

This is a common species in shady, wooded areas. It darts rapidly for short distances when disturbed and may perch head down with wings closed on the under side of leaves.

Church's Jamaican
Skipper (*Chioides
catillus churchi*)

Common Tailed
Skipper (*Urbanus
proteus*)

Evan's Jamaican
Skipper (*Polygonus
leo hagar*)

Watson's Cane Skipper
Panoquina sylvicola woodruffi
(Watson)
Wingspan: 1¹/₂ins (4cm)

Watson's Cane Skipper is an abundant skipper in open grassy areas. It is a rapid flyer and likes to sit on the upper side of leaves. The upper surface of its wings is darker than the lower. This is a widely-distributed species, from southern North America to South America.

Schaus's Skipper
Pyrrhocalles jamaicensis
(Schaus)
Wingspan: 1³/₄ins (4.5cm)

This is a widespread skipper which likes to sit on twigs and leaves in sunlight. It has a rapid flight, darting from place to place. It is the largest of the golden and black skippers on Jamica and is an endemic species.

Fiery Banded Skipper
Hylephila phyleus phyleus (Drury)
Wingspan: 1¹/₄in (3cm)

The Fiery Banded Skipper is gold and black in colour, the males having more gold than the females. It has a rapid, darting flight pattern, the males being the more active. It is widely distributed on Jamaica and is common on grasslands. It occurs from northern North America, through the West Indies and south to Argentina.

Watson's Cane Skipper
(*Panoquina sylvicola woodruffi*)

Schaus's Skipper
(*Pyrrhocalles jamaicensis*)

Fiery Banded Skipper
(*Hylephila phyleus phyleus*) (Drury)

◆ ITHOMIIDAE

The Clear Wing Butterflies

Members of this family are peculiar as most of the wing surface lacks scales, meaning that most of their colours result from refraction. The glass-like wings make it difficult to see the butterflies. They are further protected by poisons that the larvae sequester from Solanaceous plants. Only one species occurs on Jamaica.

Clear Wing (Glass Wing)
Greta diaphane diaphane
(Drury)
Wingspan: 2 ins (5 cm)

This is an uncommon butterfly, which occurs under the canopy of the forests of the Blue and John Crow Mountains. It is a weak flyer which appears as silvery blue flashes. This butterfly may be overlooked because of the transparency of its wings. It has been recorded from Jamaica and Cuba.

Clear Wing (Glass
Wing) (*Greta
diaphane diaphane*)

◆ SATYRIDAE

The Satyrs

This family closely resembles the Nymphalids. Several genera occur in Central and South America but only one in the Greater Antilles.

Jamaican Satyra
Calisto zangis (Fabricius)
Wingspan: 1³/₄ins (4.5cm)

This endemic species is the only one of this family occurring on Jamaica. It is widely distributed and prefers to 'hop' close to the ground through shrubs. The male has a prominent eye spot on the upper side of the fore wing. In the female, this is replaced by an inconspicuous dark-coloured blotch.

Jamaican Satyra
(*Calisto zangis*)

Photographing Butterflies

Photographing butterflies is a very demanding exercise, but an extremely rewarding one. Patience is essential. Remember, the butterfly is unlikely to pose for a snap shot!

To get near to butterflies, slow steady movements must be practised – always remember that these insects are very sensitive to rapid movements. You might want to start taking photographs even before you get into an ideal position, this, at least guarantees you a photograph. Watch for disturbances. Other people, other butterflies, birds, all may cause a disturbance.

In terms of equipment, macro facilities are essential. The photographs in this book were taken with a 100 mm macro lens (1:1 magnification) sometimes coupled with a x2 or x3 extender. 100 mm or 200 mm lenses are better than 50 mm as you can take the photographs from a much further distance and so you are less likely to disturb the butterfly. Fast lenses (f: 1.7) are best as you will sometimes be working under difficult lighting conditions.

A flash is useful, as you cannot always depend on natural light. A ring flash attached to the end of your lens give better results than the standard flash mounted above the lens, on the hot shoe of the camera.

The butterfly photographer must always be ready. He/she must be an opportunist, as that vital shot comes when you least expect it. Remember, if you don't have your equipment with you, you can't use it.

The camera is a very useful tool. You may bring back pictures and leave the butterfly behind. This is essential in cases where the butterfly is rare or endangered and collection undesirable.

Collecting and Preserving Butterflies

Nets

Butterfly net bags are generally made of fine muslin, allowing minimum damage to the specimens. A fine mesh is best, as the tails of some species may get trapped in the larger mesh sizes.

Nets come in a variety of sizes. The 15–18 in (38–46 cm) diameter is the most widely used. However, some lepidopterists prefer larger nets and may even use 30 in (76 cm) diameter nets. The lengths of the net handles also vary. The 6 ft (180 cm) handle is standard but they may extend to 30 ft (9 m) for collecting in the canopy.

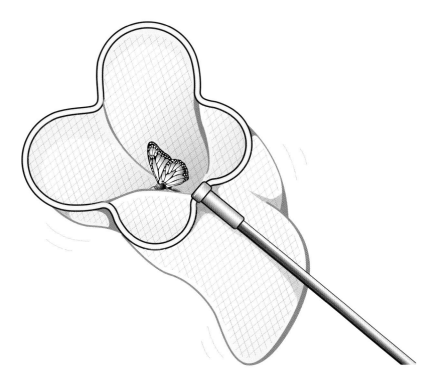

The handles and bag frame of some nets can be disassembled or folded for easy transportation. Remember, the larger the net bag and the longer the handle, the more difficult it is to manoeuvre the net.

It is often more rewarding to wait for butterflies to settle before attempting to net them.

Collecting by hand

Butterflies often settle with their wings closed. In such cases, it might be possible to collect a specimen using the thumb and index finger. The hand movement must be very slow and steady; butterflies react to quick movements much more readily. The insect is collected by the thorax, never by the wing.

Selecting the specimen

The collector aims at specimens that are in a perfect condition (*i.e.* A1 specimens). A1 specimens are best obtained by rearing from a pupa. It is often possible to clearly see the specimen before collection by a net and so determine if it is badly damaged. In other cases it might be possible to examine the specimen while it is in the net and before it is killed. Poor quality specimens can then be released.

Laws, regulations and institutions

The collector should always be aware of the laws/regulations governing the collection of butterflies. On Jamaica these regulations are set out by the Natural Environmental Planning Agency (NEPA). The IUCN also sets regulations. Presently, regulations prohibit the collection of the endangered *Papilio homerus*. In general, excessive collection should be avoided.

Insect collections are housed at the Department of Life Sciences, University of the West Indies, and at the Natural History Museum of the Institute of Jamaica. Collectors are urged to work in co-operation with these institutions and to make contributions to their collections.

Preserving the specimens

Each specimen should be transferred from the net to an envelope of waxed paper (waxed paper reduces loss of scales) and the envelope placed in a sturdy container (pan or box) for safe transportation. It is often useful to have the container attached to your belt in such a manner that envelopes can be retrieved and replaced rapidly with minimum inconvenience.

Specimens may be kept in the envelopes or they may be displayed on pins. In the latter case, specimens should be pinned as soon as possible before they become dry or they will have to be softened before the wings can be spread. All specimens must be carefully labeled with the locality, parish, date and the collector's name. Additional data such as the weather conditions and any behaviour patterns may be useful, but are optional. Remember, an insect without information on the date and locality of collection loses much of its scientific value.

The collector would be advised to use high quality insect pins and boxes. Poor quality pins will eventually rust and important specimens might be damaged. Pins come in a variety of sizes, numbered 000 to 6 (6 being the largest). Numbers 1, 2 and 3 are most commonly used.

Well-made boxes are essential as they keep out pests such as book lice, silver fishes and Dermestid beetles which attack collections. The butterfly collection *must* be protected from these insects. Most collectors use paradichlorobenzene (PDB) or crushed mothballs (Naphthalene). However, periodically freezing the collection for one or two hours is rapidly becoming a popular method.

Appendix

Taxonomic Checklist of Jamaican Butterflies

In accordance with the International Code of Zoological Nomenclature, the names of species and genera are written in *italics*. The name(s) of the author(s) who described the species are placed, at the end of the species' name. The author's name is enclosed in parentheses when the genus in which a butterfly is now placed is different from that in which it was originally described.

The names of the families are written in capitals. If the species is well known by another generic or specific name it is included in parentheses.

Family and species	Endemic (end)	Endemic subspecies (end/sub)
DANAIDAE		
Danaus cleophile (Godart)		
Danaus eresimus eresimus (Cramer)		
Danaus gilippus jamaicensis (Bates)		X
Danaus plexippus (Linnaeus)		
ITHOMIIDAE		
Greta diaphane diaphane (Drury)		X
SATYRIDAE		
Calisto zangis (Fabricius)	X	
NYMPHALIDAE		
Adelpha abyla (Hewitson)	X	
Agraulis (Dione) vanillae insularis Linnaeus		
Anaea (troglodyta) portia Fabricius	X	
Anaea johnsoni Avinoff and Shoumatoff		X
Anartia jatrophae jamaicensis Moschler		X
Anthanasa (Phyciodes) frisia Poey		
Anttillea (Phyciodes) proclea (Doubleday and Hewitson)	X	
Atlantea pantoni (Kaye)	X	
Colobura dirce avinoffi Comstock		X
Dione (Agraulis) vanillae Linnaeus		
Doxocopa laure fabricii Hall		X
Dryas iulia delila (Fabricius)		X
Dynamine egaea egaea (Fabricius)	X	
Eunica monima (Cramer)		
Eunica tatila tatilista Kaye		

Euptoieta claudia claudia (Cramer)		
Euptoieta hegesia hegesia (Cramer) Godart	X	
Hamadryas amphichloe (februa) Biosduval		
Heliconius charitonius simulator Rober		X
Historis acheronta cadmus (Fabricius)		X
Historis odius odius (Fabricius)		
Hypanartia paullus (Fabricius)		
Hypolimnas misippus (Linnaeus)		
Junonia (Precis) genoveva (Cramer)		
Junonia (Precis) evarete (Stoll)		
Libytheana (carinenta) terena (Godart)		
Lucinia cadma Drury	X	
Marpesia chiron Fabricius		
Marpesia eleuchea pellenis (Godart)		X
Mestra dorcas Fabricius	X	
Phyciodes (Antillea) proclea (Doubleday and Hewitson)	X	
Phyciodes (Antillea) pelops anaccaona (Fabricius)		
Siproeta stelenes stelenes (Linnaeus)		
Vanessa atalanta Linnaeus		
Vanessa cardui (Linnaeus)		
Vanessa virginiensis (Drury)		
LYCAENIDAE		
Brephidium exilis isophthalma (Herrich-Schaffer)		
Callophrys (Cyanophrys) crethona (Hewitson)		X
Chlorostrymon maesites maesites (Herrich-Schaffer)		
Chlorostrymon simaethis jago (Comstock and Huntington)		X
Electrostrymon angelia pantoni (Comstock and Huntington)		X
Electrostrymon (Strymon) pan (Drury)	X	
Hemiargus (Cyclargus) dominica (Moschler)	X	
Hemiargus (Cyelargus) ammon ammon (Lucas)		
Hemiargus hanno ceraunus (Fabricius)		
Leptotes cassius theonus (Lucas)		
Leptotes perkinsae Kaye	X	
Ministrymon azia (Hewitson)		
Nesiostrymon shoumatofi (Comstock and Huntington)		X
Rekoa (Heterosmaitia) bourkei (Kaye)		
Strymon acis gossei (Comstock and Huntington)		X
Strymon bazochii gundlachianus Bates		

Strymon columella cybira (Hewitson) *Strymon limenia* (Hewitson) *Strymon martialis* (Herrich-Schaffer)		
PIERIDAE *Anteos clorinde nivifera* (Fruhstorfer) *Anteos maerula maerula* (Fabricius) *Aphrissa godartiana hartonia* Butler *Aphrissa statira cubana* d'Almeida *Appias (Glutophrissa) drusilla jacksoni* Kaye *Ascia (Ganyra) josephina paramaryllis* Comstock *Ascia monuste eubotea* Godart *Eurema adamsi* (Lathy) *Eurema daira palmira* Poey *Eurema dina parvumbra* Kaye *Eurema elathea* (Cramer) *Eurema lisa euterpe* (Menetries) . *Eurema messalina messalina* (Fabricius) *Eurema nicippe* (Cramer) *Eurema nise* (Cramer) *Eurema proterpia proterpia* (Fabricius) *Kricogonia castalia* (Fabricius) *Kricogonia lyside* (Godart) *Nathalis iole* Boisduval *Phoebis agarithe antillia* Brown *Phoebis argante* Avinoff *Phoebis philea philea* (Johansson) *Phoebis sennae sennae* (Linnaeus)	X X 	 X
PAPILIONIDAE *Eurytides (Graphium, Protesilaus) marcellinus* (Doubleday) *Papilio andraemon* (Hubner) *Papilio (Pterourus) homerus* Fabricius *Papilio pelaus pelaus* Fabricius *Papilio (Heraclides) thersites* Fabricius *Papilio (Heraclides) thoas melonius* (Rothschild & Jordan) *Battus polydamas jamaicensis* (Rothschild & Jordan)	X X X X X X	
HESPERIIDAE *Achlyodes mithridates mithridates* (Fabricius) *Aguna asander jasper* Evans *Anastrus sempiternus dilloni* Bell and Comstock *Antigonus nearchus* (Latreille)	X	

Astraptes anaphus anausis (Godman and Salvin)		
Astraptes talus (Cramer)		
Astraptes jaira (Butler)		
Autochton neis (Geyer)		
Cabares potrillo potrillo (Lucas)		
Calpodes ethlius (Stoll)		
Chioides catillus churchi Bell and Comstock		
Choranthus lilliae Bell		
Cogia calchas (Herrich-Schaffer)		
Cymaenes tripunctus tripunctus (Herrich-Schaffer)		
Epargyreus antaeus Hewitson		
Ephyriades arcas philemon (Fabricius)		
Ephyriades brunnea jamaicensis (Moschler)		X
Ephyriades zephodes (Hubner)		
Euphyes singularis insolata (Butler)		
Gesta gesta gesta (Herrich-Schaffer)		
Grais stigmaticus juncta Evans	X	
Heliopetes arsalte arsalte (Linnaeus)		
Hylephila phyleus phyleus (Drury)		
Lerodea eufala eufala (Edwards)		
Nisoniades bessus bessus (Moschler)		
Nyctelius nyctelius nyctelius (Latreille)		
Ouleus fridericus trina Geyer		
Panoquina fusina jumbo Evans		
Panoquina ocola (Edwards)		
Panoquina panoquinoides panoquinoides (Skinner)		
Panoquina sylvicola woodruffi (Watson)		
Perichares philetes philetes (Gmelin)		
Phocides perkinsi (Kaye)	X	
Phocides pigmalion batabano Lucas		
Polygonus leo hagar Evans	X	
Proteides mercurius jamaicensis Skinner		X
Pyrgus oileus (Linnaeus)		
Pyrrhocalles jamaicensis (Schaus)	X	
Rhinthon cubana cubana (Herrich-Schaffer)		
Synapte malitiosa malitiosa (Herrich-Schaffer)		
Timochares ruptifasciata runia Evans		
Urbanus albimargo takuta (Mabille)		
Urbanus proteus (Linnaeus)		
Urbanus teleus (Hubner)		
Urbanus tanna Evans		
Vettius fantasos fantasos (Stoll)		
Wallengrenia (otho) vesuria (Plotz)	X	

Suppliers of Entomological Equipment

BioQuip Products
17803 Lasalle Avenue
California 90248-3602
USA

Carolina Biological Supply Co.
2700 York Road
Burlington
North Carolina 27215
USA

Watkins and Doncaster
P.O. Box 5
Cranbrook
Kent TN18 5EZ
England

Forestry Supplies Inc.
International Sales Division
205 W. Rankin Street
P.O. Box 8397
Jackson
MS 39284-8397
USA

Useful Addresses

Natural History Society of Jamaica
Department of Life Sciences
University of the West Indies
Mona
Kingston 7
Jamaica
West Indies

The NHSJ, since its inception in 1940, has been active in the study and conservation of butterflies on Jamaica. Its publications, *Natural History Notes* and the *Jamaica Naturalist*, contain valuable information. The Department of Life Sciences houses an insect collection and is the primary research institution on Jamaica.

Natural Environmental Planning Agency (NEPA)
5 Caledonia Avenue
Kingston 5
Jamaica
West Indies

NEPA regulates all matters relating to collecting on Jamaica. Visiting collectors should contact this Authority for permits.

Natural History Division
Institute Of Jamaica
12 East Street
Kingston
Jamaica
West Indies

The IOJ houses the national insect collection, which dates back to the beginning of this century.

Index of Common Names

Index of Scientific Names

abyla, Adelpha, 26
acheronta cadmus, Historis, 30
acis gossei, Strymon, 50
Adelpha abyla, 26
agarithe antillia, Phoebis, 68, 70
Agraulis (Dione) vanillae
    insularis, 42
Anaea portia, 32
anaphus anausis, Astraptes, 88
Anartia jatrophae, 20
andraemon, Papilio (Heraclides), 74
Angelia pantoni, Electrostrymon, 52
Anteos maerula maerula, 70
Anthanassa (Phyciodes) frisia, 40
Antillea (Phyciodes) proclea, 40
Aphrissa godartiana hartonia, 72
—— *statira cubana,* 72
Appias drusilla castalia Fabricus, 56
argante, Phoebis, 70
Ascia monuste eubotea, 54
—— *josephina paramaryllis,* 56
Astraptes anaphus anausis, 88
—— *jaira,* 88
Atlantea pantoni, 44

Battus polydamas jamaicensis, 76, 79
Brephidium exilis isophthalma, 12, 48
Buckeye, 36

Calisto zangis, 96
cassius theonus, Leptotes, 46
catillus, Chiodies, 90
charitonus simulator, Heliconius, 22, 25
Chiodies catillus, 90
claudia claudia, Euptoieta, 34
Colobura dirce avinoffi, 26
columella cybira, Strymon, 50

daira palmira, Eurema, 63
Danaus cleophile, 18
—— *eresimus,* 17
—— *gilippus,* 18
—— *plexippus,* 16
diaphane diaphane, Greta, 94
dina, Eurema, 67
Dione. See *Agraulis vanillae*
    insularis.
dirce avinoffi, Colobura, 26
dorcas, Mestra, 34
drusilla castalia, Appias, 56
Dryas iulia delia, 42
Dynamine egaea egaea, 28

egaea egaea, Dynamine, 28
elathea, Eurema, 63, 65
Electrostrymon (Strymon) pan, 52
—— *pantontangelia,*
eleuchea pellenis, Marpesia, 24
eresimus, Danaus, 17
Euptoieta claudia claudia, 34
—— *hegesia hegesia,* 36
Eurema daira palmira, 63
—— *dina,* 63
—— *elathea,* 63, 65
—— *lisa euterpe,* 59
—— *nicippe,* 61
—— *nise,* 61
—— *proterpia proterpia,* 65
Eurytides (Graphium Protesilaus)
    marcellinus, 80
evarete, Junonia, 38
exilis isophthalma, Brephidium, 48

frisia, Anthanassa (Phyciodes), 40

genoveva, Junonia, 36, *38*
gilippus, Danaus, 18

godartiana hartonia, Aphrissa, 72
Greta diaphane diaphane, 94

hanno ceraunus, Hemiargus, 46
hegesia hegesia, Euptoieta, 36
Heliconius charitonius simulator,
    22, 25
Hemiargus hanno ceraunus, 46
Historis acheronta cadmus, 30
—— odius odius, 30
homerus, Papilio, 4, 8, 12, 82–86
Hylephila phyleus phyleus, 92

iulia delila, Dryas, 42
iole Boisduval, Natalis, 58

jatrophae, Anartia, 20
jaira, Astraptes, 88
josephina paramaryllis, Ascia, 56
Junonia (Precis) evarete, 38
—— (Precis) genoveva, 36, 38

Kricogonia lyside, 54

leo, Polygonus, 90
Leptotes cassius theonus, 46
lisa euterpe, Eurema, 59
lyside, Kricogonia, 54

maerula maerula, Anteos, 72
marcellinus, Eurytides, 80
Marpesia eleuchea pellenis, 24
Mestra dorcas, 34
monuste eubotea, Ascia, 54

Natalis iole Boisduval, 58
nicippe, Eurema, 61
nise, Eurema, 61

odius odius, Historis, 30
oielus, Pyrgus, 88

pan, Electrostrymon (Strymon), 52

Panoquina sylvicola, 92
pantoni, Atlantea, 44
——, Electrostrymon, 52
Papilio (Heraclides) andraemon, 74
—— homerus, 4, 8, 12, 82–86
—— (Heraclides) pelaus pelaus, 78
—— (Heraclides) thersites, 74
—— (Heraclides) thoas melonius, 76
pelaus pelaus, Papilio, 68, 70
Phoebis agarithe antillia, 70
—— argante, 70
—— sennae, 66
phyleus phyleus, Hylephila, 92
plexippus, Danaus, 16
polydamas jamaicensis, Battus, 76, 79
Polygonus leo, 90
portia, Anaea, 32
proclea, Antillea (Phyciodes), 40
proterpia proterpia, Eurema, 65
proteus, Urbanus, 90
Pyrgus oielus, 88
Pyrrhocalles jamaicensis, 92

sennae, Phoebis, 66
Siproeta stelenes stelenes, 22
statira cubana, Aphrissa, 70
stelenes stelenes, Siproeta, 22
Strymon acis gossei, 50
—— columella cybira, 50
—— pan. See Electrostrymon
    (Strymon) pan.
sylvicola, Panoquina, 92

thersites, Papilio (Heraclides), 74
thoas melonius, Papilio, 76

Urbanus proteus, 90

Vanessa virginensis, 20
vanillae insularis, Agraulis (Dione), 42
virginensis, Vanessa, 20

zangis, Calisto, 96